The Pearl of Great Price

D0314076

Written by Bethan Lycett

Illustrated by Hannah Stout

This is a story that Jesus told,

Of a man who loved searching for jewels and gold.

His job as a jeweller meant travelling around,

Buying the wonderful things that he found.

While travelling India he found a small ring,

A shiny red ruby that made his heart sing.

"I must have this ruby, its beauty is great."

So he paid for it quickly, he just couldn't wait.

In Persia a fine amber belt was revealed,

As soon as he saw it the jeweller squealed!

"I must have that belt as it shines like the sun."

So he paid for it quickly, the deal had been done.

A shimmering diamond of yellow and white,

Was found when in Africa, dazzling so bright.

"I must have this diamond, it shines like a star."

So he paid for it quickly, his favourite so far.

In Egypt he found a
green emerald pin,
Which glowed
in the light and made
his eyes spin.

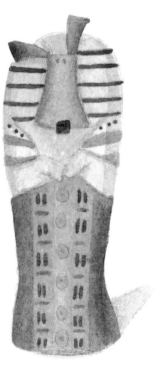

"I must have this pin for my new cashmere coat."

So he paid for it quickly, then jumped on his boat.

Some sparkling blue sapphires from Australia were found,
And onto the jeweller's head they were crowned.

"I must have this crown with its sapphires of blue."

So he paid for it quickly, and took it home too.

In Brazil was a **necklace** on a street market stall,
Each bright purple **amethyst** tiny and small.

"I must have this necklace,
it matches my socks!"

So he paid for it quickly, and placed it
into his box.

One day as he travelled
his mouth opened wide,

"That's it, that's the one!"
he suddenly cried.

The pearl was the finest
thing he'd ever seen

Its orient: blue, yellow,
purple and green!

So perfect and round,
and oh, how it gleamed.

The most beautiful gem
that ever he'd dreamed.

"I must sell my jewels, my house, all I own,

For a gem that's more precious than any I've known."

All that he had was taken and sold,

Everything went, even silver and gold.

He paid for the pearl and he held it so tight;

And he never let go, by day or by night.

Jesus is like the pearl in the story, so precious that He is worth more than anything in the world.

The Bible teaches us that all those who have trusted in Jesus to forgive their sins need to put Him above everything else in their lives.

Just like the jeweller in the story, Jesus was also willing
to give everything, even His life on the cross,
to make us His own. We are so precious to Jesus that
He will never let go of those who have trusted in Him.

The Bible tells us
from the love God has for us.
"nothing can separate us
Not death, not life, not angels, not ruling spirits, nothing now,
nothing in the future, no powers,

"... nothing above us, nothing below us, or anything else in the whole world will ever be able to separate us from the love of God that is in Christ Jesus our Lord."

Romans 8:38–39

"The kingdom of heaven is like a man looking for fine pearls. One day he found a very valuable pearl. The man went and sold everything he had to buy that pearl."

Matthew 13:45–46

For Thomas, Charlotte, Emily and Beatrix

The Pearl of Great Price

Text and Illustrations © 2016. Bethan Lycett and Hannah Stout.

All rights reserved. Except as may be permitted by the Copyright Act, no part of this publication may be reproduced in any form or by any means without prior permission from the publisher.

Scriptures quoted from the International Children's Bible®,
copyright ©1986, 1988, 1999, 2015 by Tommy Nelson. Used by permission.

Published by 10Publishing, a division of 10ofThose Limited.
ISBN 978-1-910587-63-8

Typeset by: Diane Warnes
Printed in the UK.

10Publishing, a division of 10ofthose.com
Unit C, Tomlinson Road, Leyland, Lancashire, PR25 2DY England
Email: info@10ofthose.com
Website: www.10ofthose.com